Pam Wedgwood

Piano Basics Workouts

Fun warm-ups and technical exercises for the beginner pianist

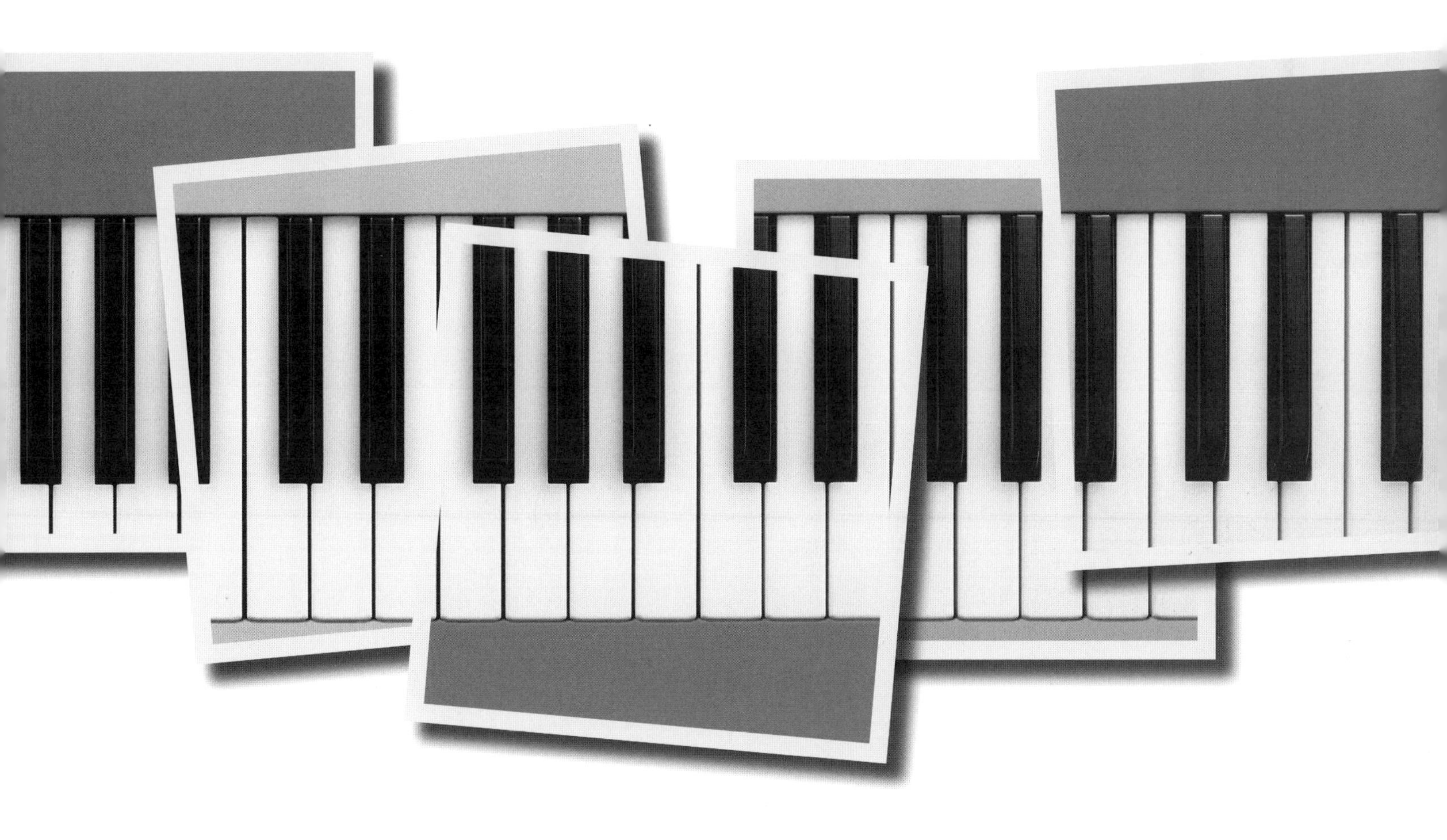

5.50

This edition first published in 2014
Bloomsbury House
74–77 Great Russell Street
London WC1B 3DA
Cover designed by Chloë Alexander
Book designed by Sue Clarke
Printed in England by Caligraving Ltd

ISBN10: 0-571-53836-3
EAN13: 978-0-571-53836-2

To buy Faber Music publications or to find out about the full range of titles available please contact your local music retailer or Faber Music sales enquiries:

Faber Music Ltd, Burnt Mill, Elizabeth Way, Harlow CM20 2HX
Tel: +44 (0) 1279 82 89 82 Fax: +44 (0) 1279 82 89 83
sales@fabermusic.com fabermusicstore.com

Introduction

This piano course has been specifically written for children from around age 8 upwards, with the intention of developing musicianship skills alongside their piano playing. The dice which you will spot throughout highlight the different aspects of musicianship that are covered alongside the pieces:

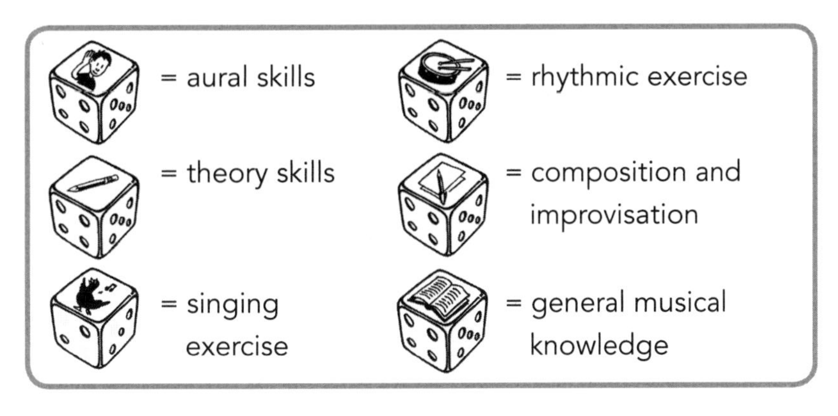

In addition there are many teaching ideas, hints and tips included on *fabermusicstore.com/basics* to add to and stimulate your teaching.

All music by Pam Wedgwood unless otherwise stated.

Clapping duets
You clap the upper stave and your teacher claps the lower for both of these pieces.

Ground control: all five fingers

Play slowly at first, keeping a steady, even pulse.

Prepare to play this piece by resting piano-playing shaped hands on a flat surface.
Try lifting your fourth and fifth fingers without raising your other fingers. It's tricky!

Ground control: fourth and fifth fingers

This exercise will get your fourth and fifth fingers working.
Make sure your thumbs don't wander from their position.

Make up some words to fit the mood and rhythm of the right-hand part, then sing them.

Dual control in three time

Always try to look ahead and prepare your fingers.
Play hands separately and slowly at first.

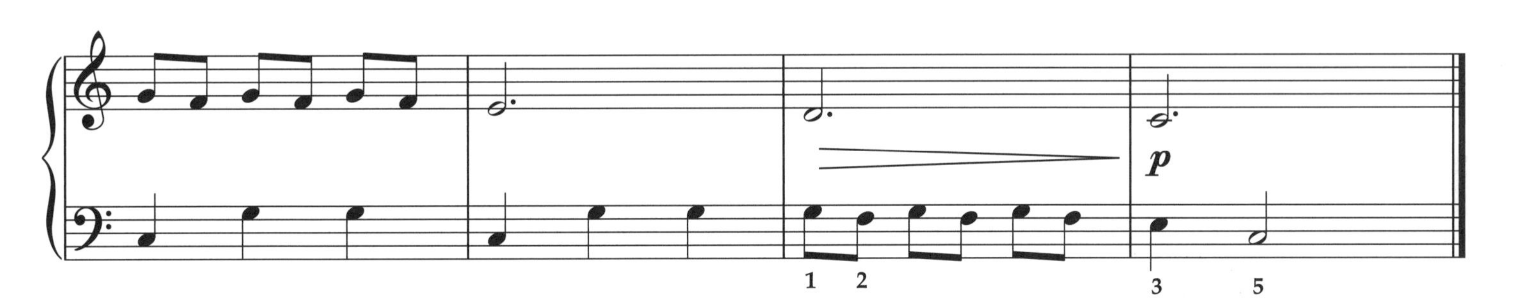

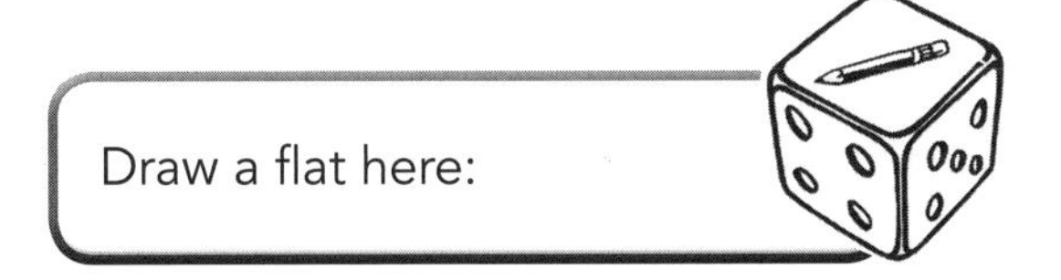

Draw a flat here:

Sing back each two-bar phrase after you've played it.

Black-note control

Find all the B flats on your piano: how many are there?

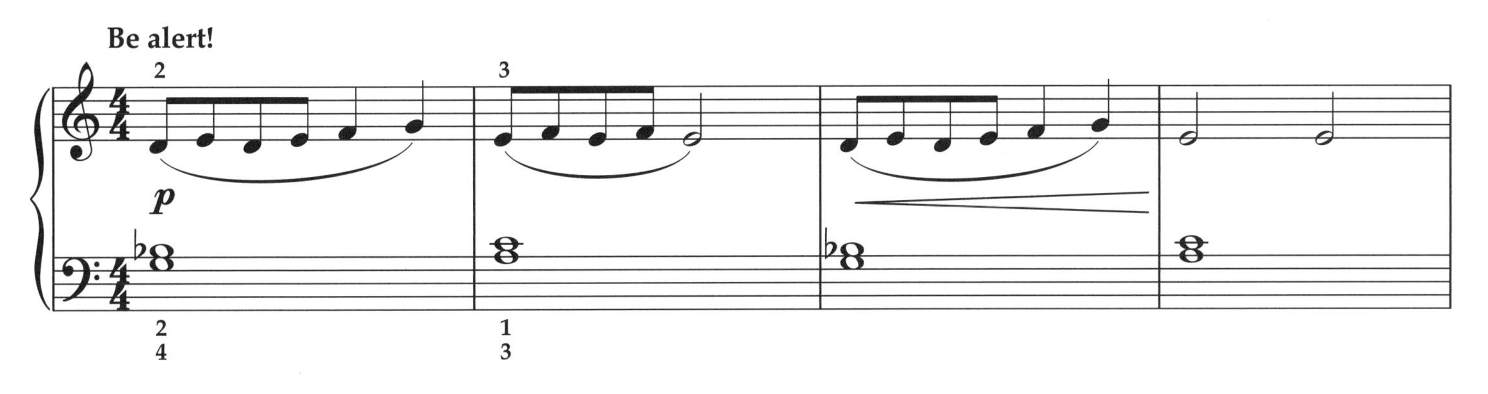

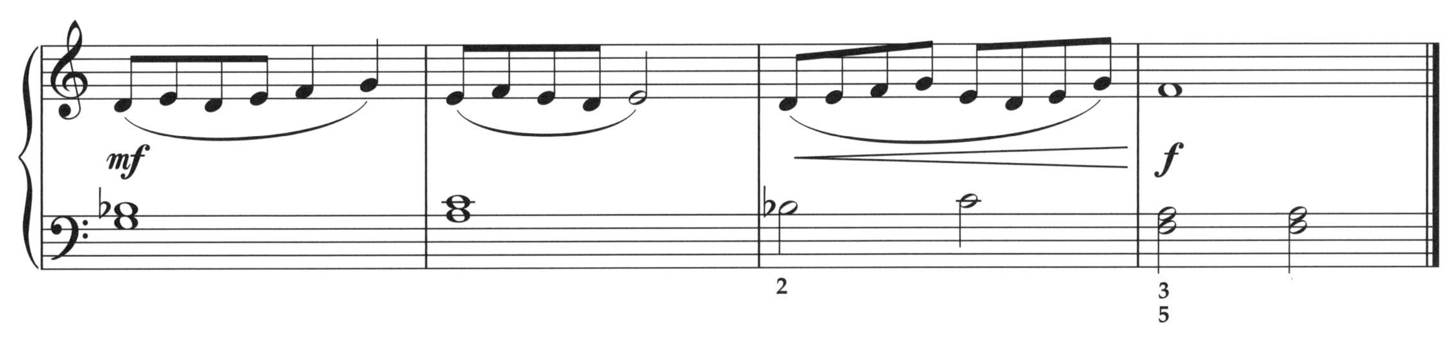

Draw a crotchet rest here:

Draw a sharp here:

Stretch control

Extending your hands.

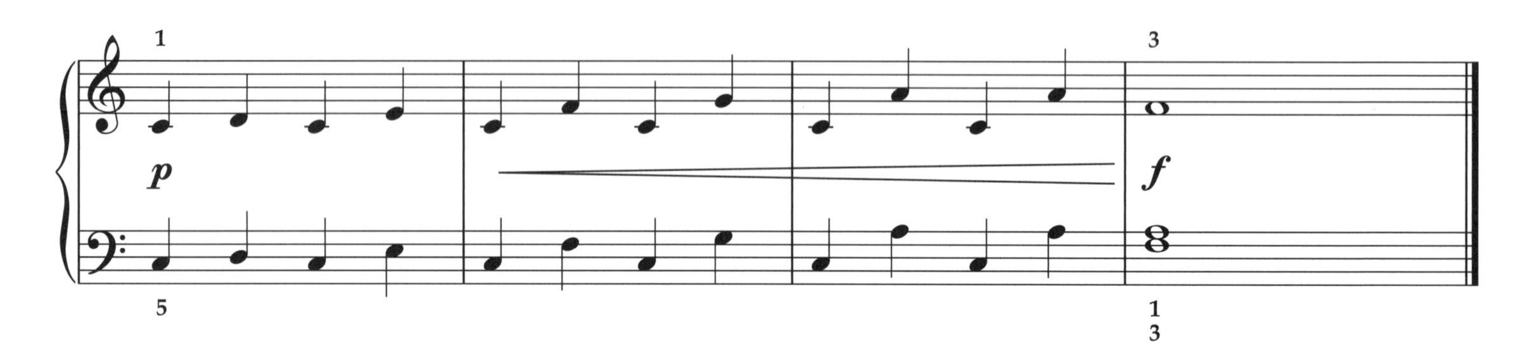

Fact file **Remember** ♩. = 1½ counts

Black note alert: look out for F sharps!
Find all the F sharps on your piano.
How many are there?

Try this piece as a clapping duet with your teacher.

Dotted control

Ground control to major scale

Stay relaxed and let your fingers and thumb glide easily.

Can you name all the notes in these scales?

Write the note names in under bar 1 and over bar 3 in the next piece.

Complete scale control

Always play your scales with relaxed fingers and wrists.

Traffic running smoothly

Don't forget that a sharp sign lasts right through the bar.

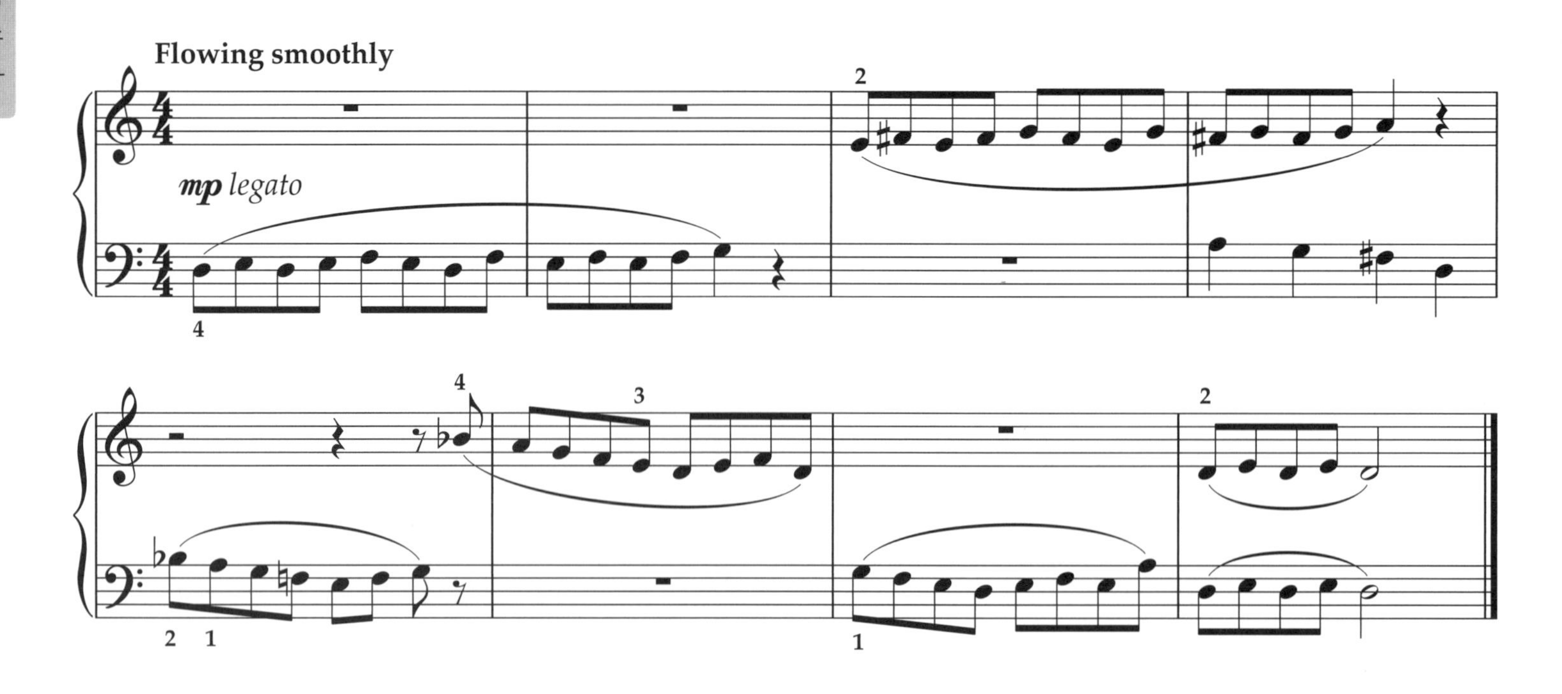

Fact file A natural sign (♮) cancels the sharp or flat before it.

How many of these can you see in the next piece?

Sharp signs =

Flat signs =

Natural signs =

Speed control ahead

Do try this hands separately first.

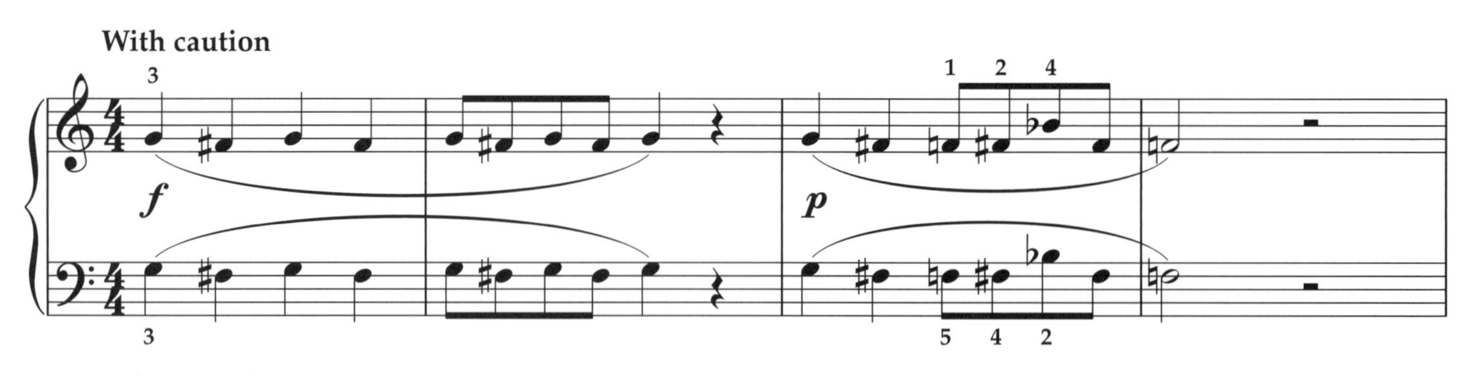

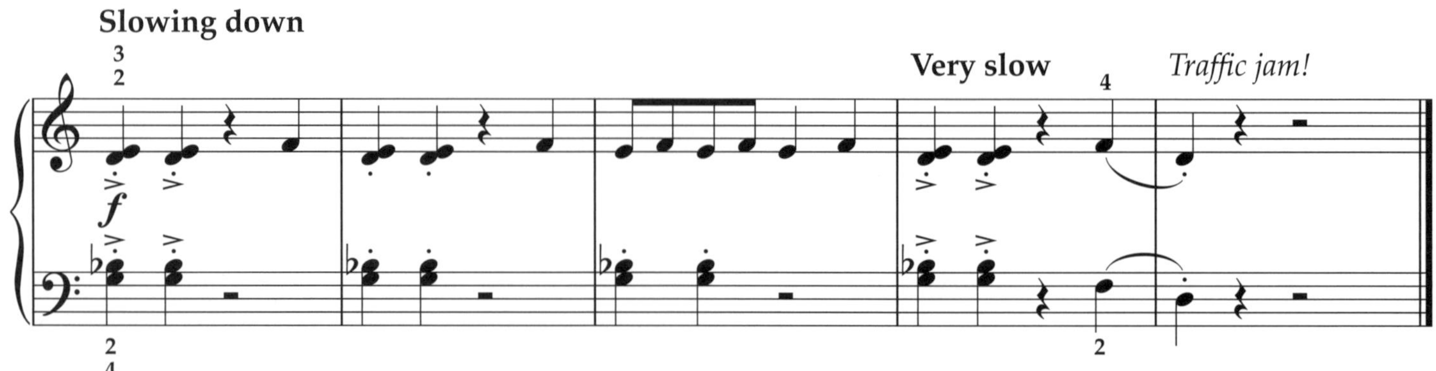

Ground zero to lower notes
With a spring
mp (2nd f)
1.
2.
poco rit.
Boogie bass control
When you know this piece well, try improvising a right-hand part to fit it. Keep it really simple!
Rhythmically
mf
G force
With strength
f
poco rit.
ff
low G

Arpeggio control

This workout uses all the notes of the broken chord of C major.

Relaxed

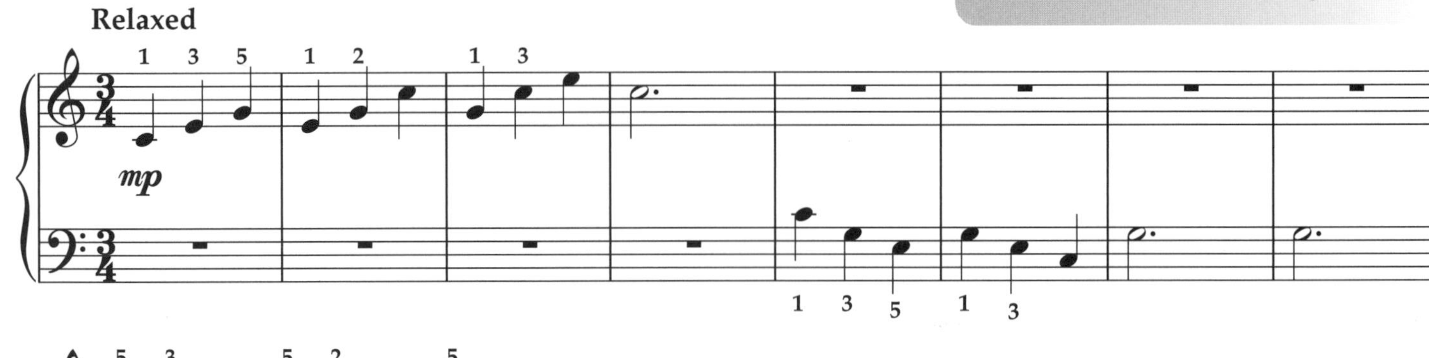

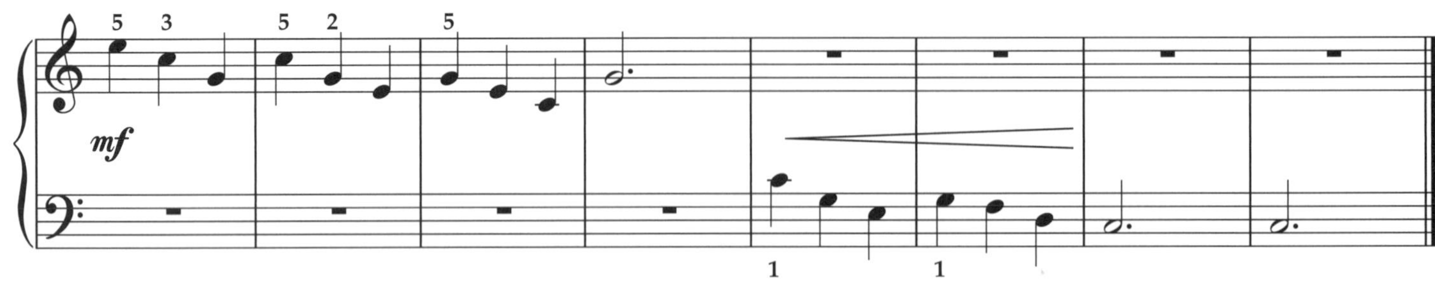

Your teacher will play the first phrase of this piece, and then again with one change.

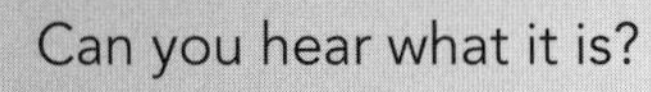

Can you hear what it is?

Right hand on patrol

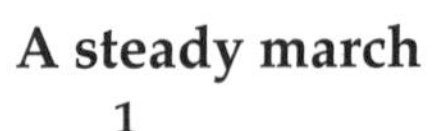

A steady march

Left hand on patrol

A steady march

Walking in muddy boots

Can you name the notes in the first two bars of these two pieces?

Walking in puddles

Fact file The small note in the last bar is a crushed note – play it quickly before the main note.

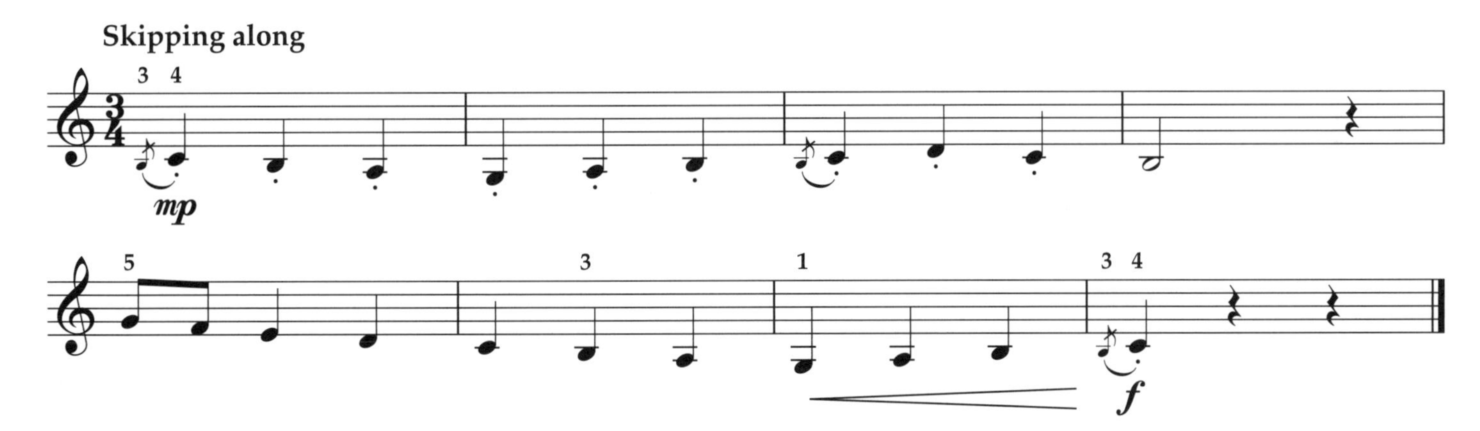

Walking through the jungle

Try this piece as a clapping duet with your teacher.

A minor situation

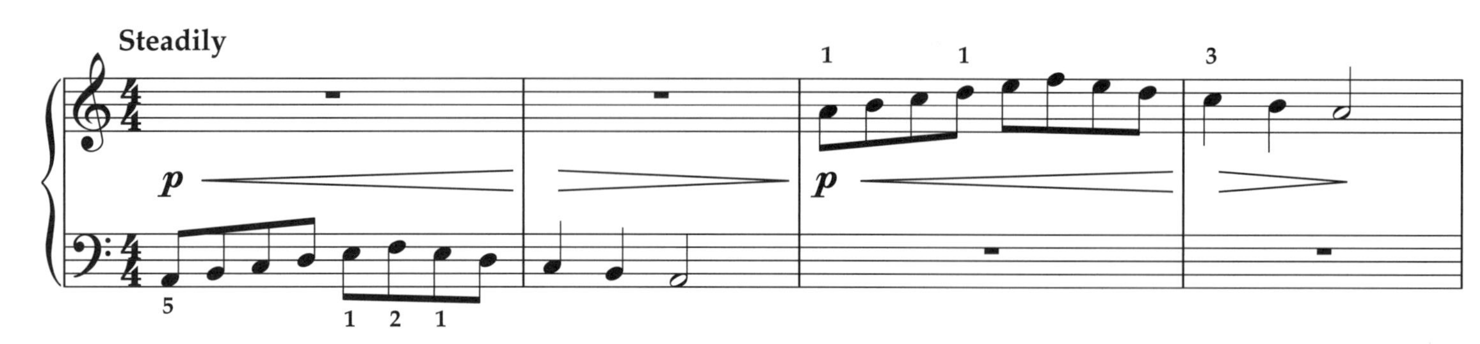

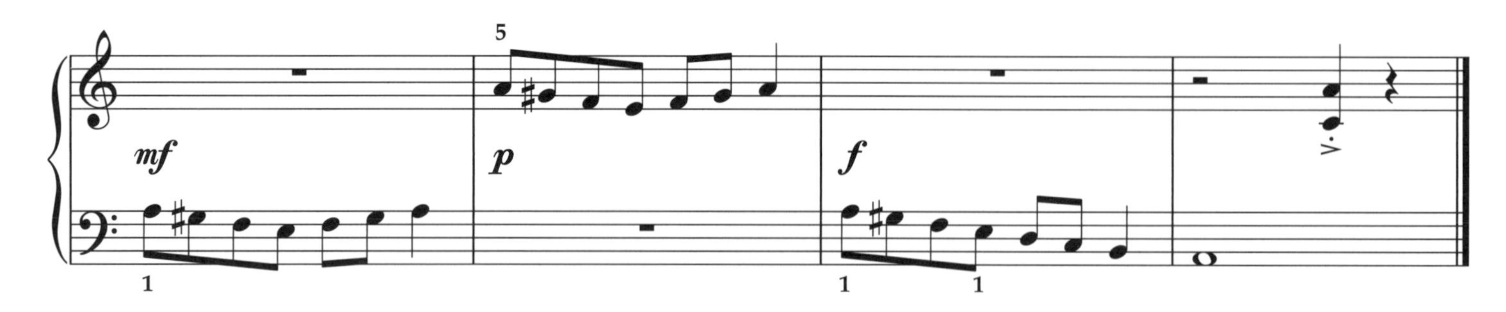

Right-hand control

Keep your fingers nice and rounded for the A minor arpeggio – like there's a bubble underneath your hand. Flat fingers won't work.

Left-hand control

Dance of the grizzly bear

Sing back each of these phrases after you've played it.

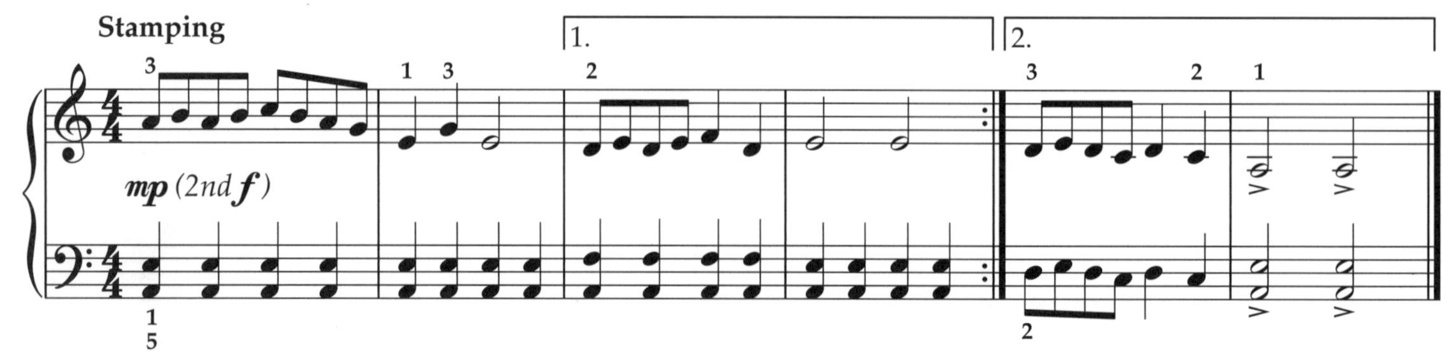

Floating

Here your left hand is playing in the treble clef.

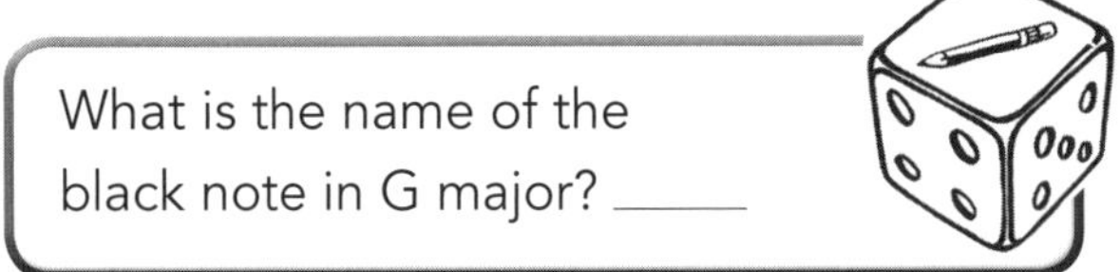

G major rumba

A **rumba** is a dance from Cuba. The name comes from the word *rumbo* which means 'party'.

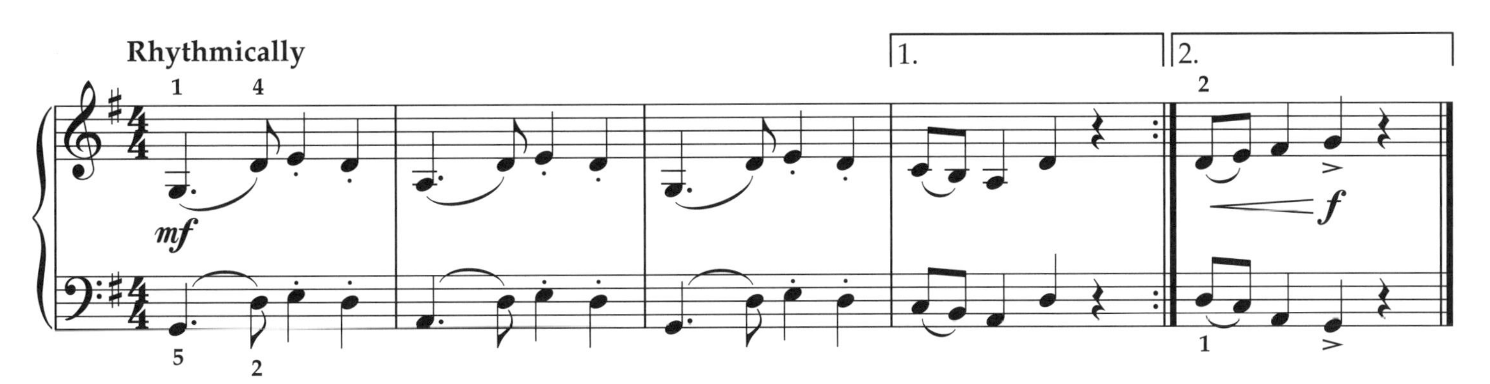

Over the top!

Keep your left hand hovering, ready to play.

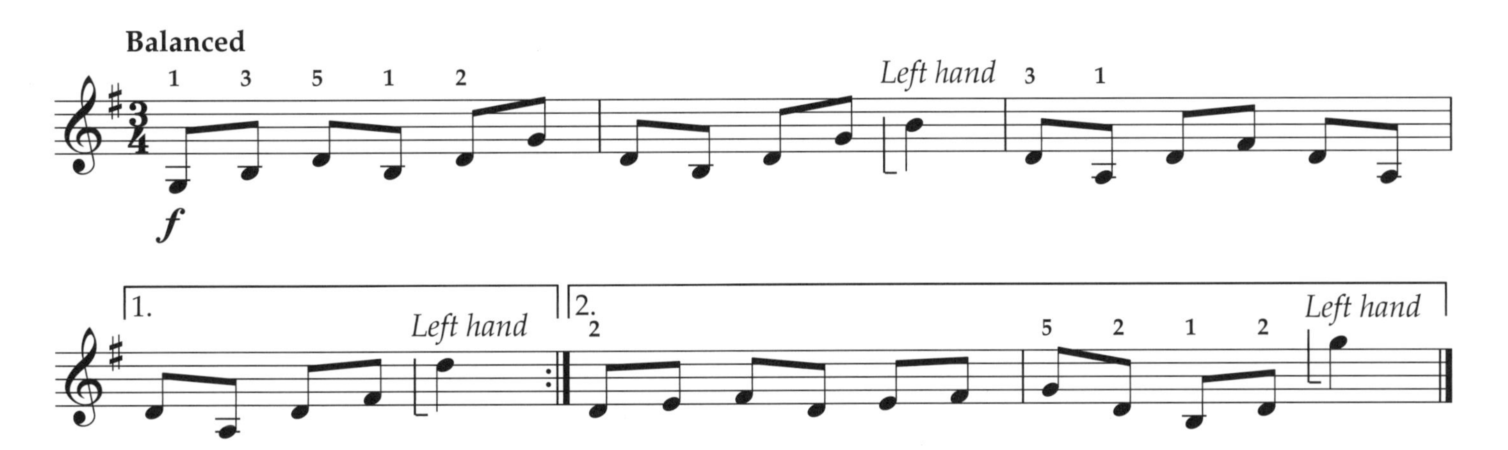

F major has one flat in the key signature.

Write it here: ________

F major in control

Sleeping

Control the sound when you play pianissimo – but don't slow down.

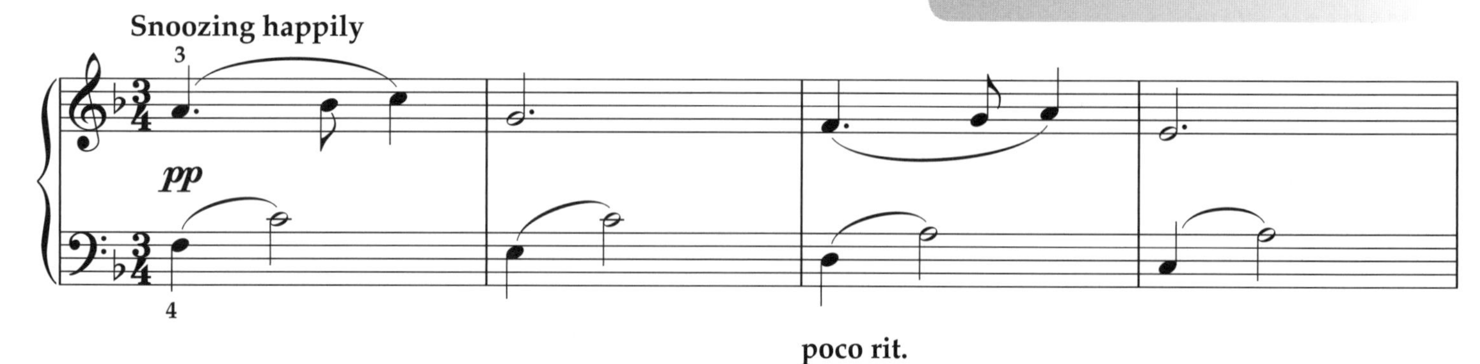

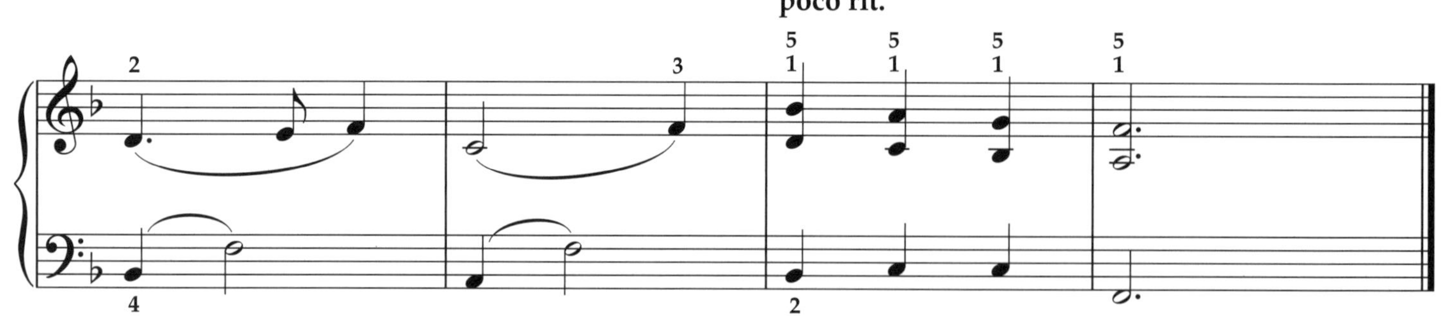

Hit the road

Be very careful that you don't speed up when you are playing fortissimo.

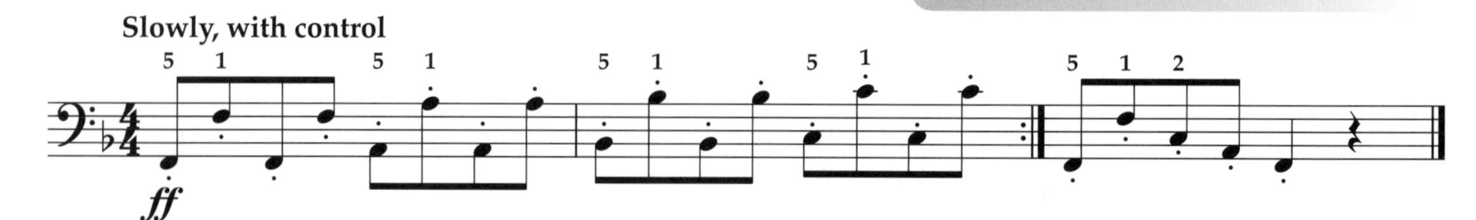

D minor situation

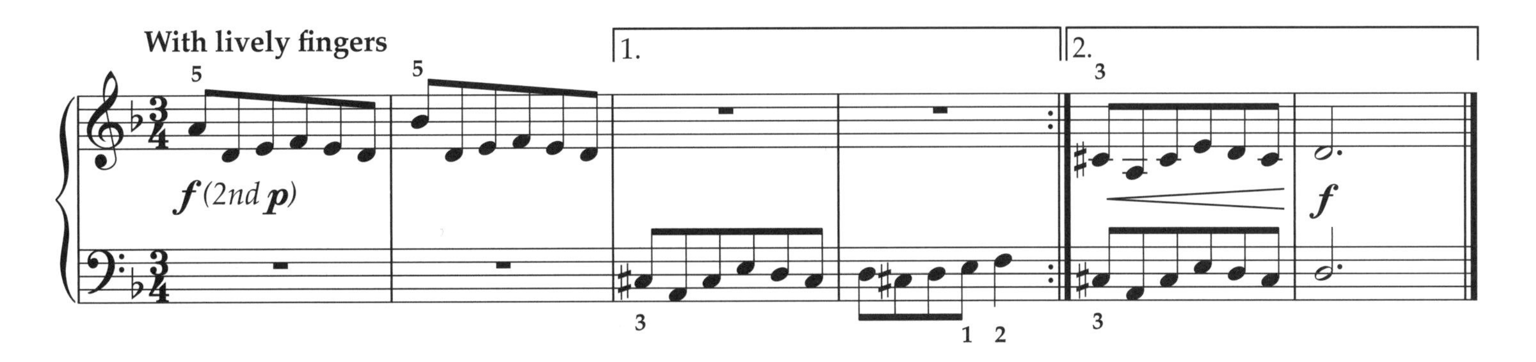

This is from a famous piano piece by **Ludwig van Beethoven** called *Für Elise* (which means 'For Elise').

A touch of Beethoven

This piece requires good finger control.
Practise it hands separately first!

Which black keys do you need in this piece?
Find where they are before you start playing.

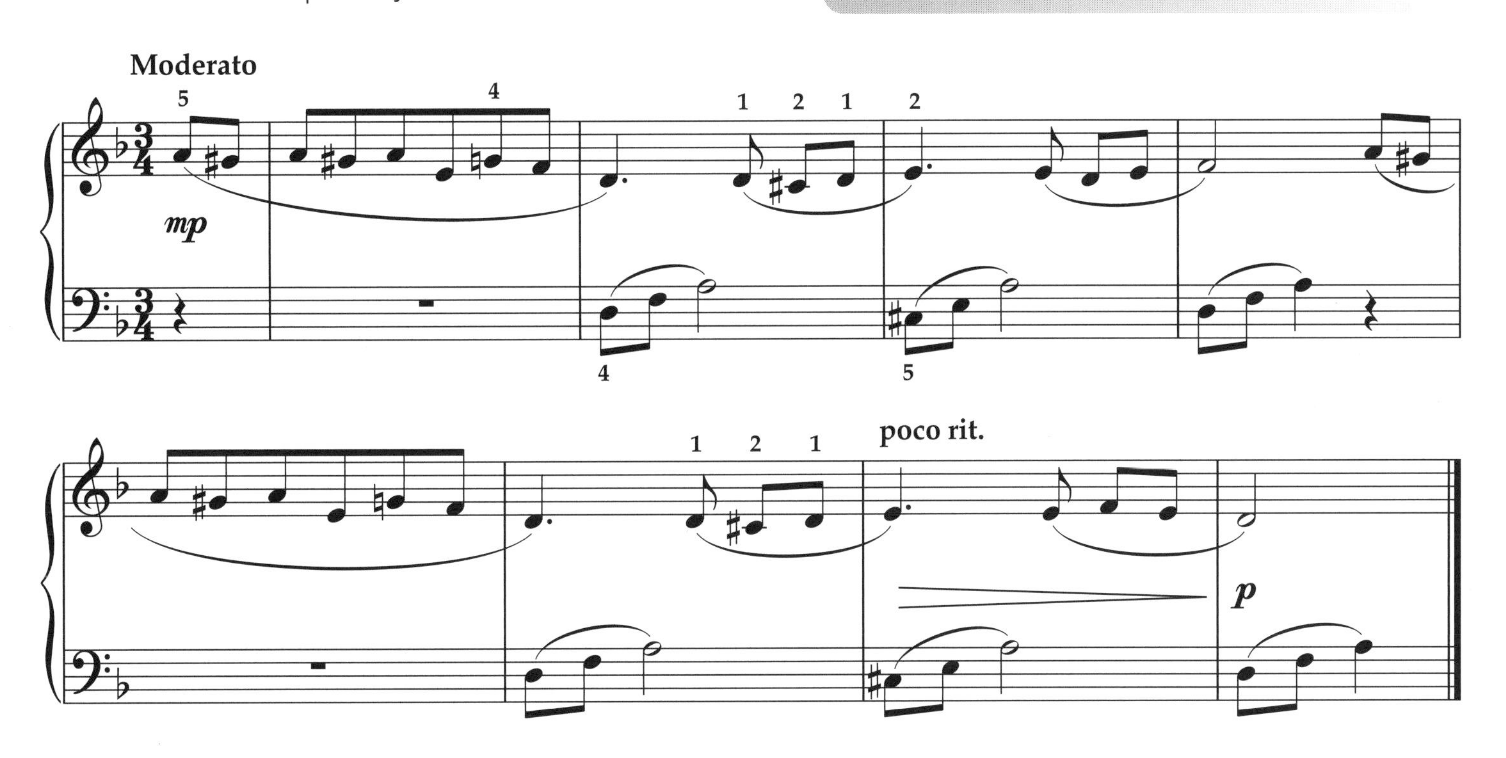

Contraflow

Play this firmly, but with relaxed fingers.

Broken-chord workout

Name the key of each line.

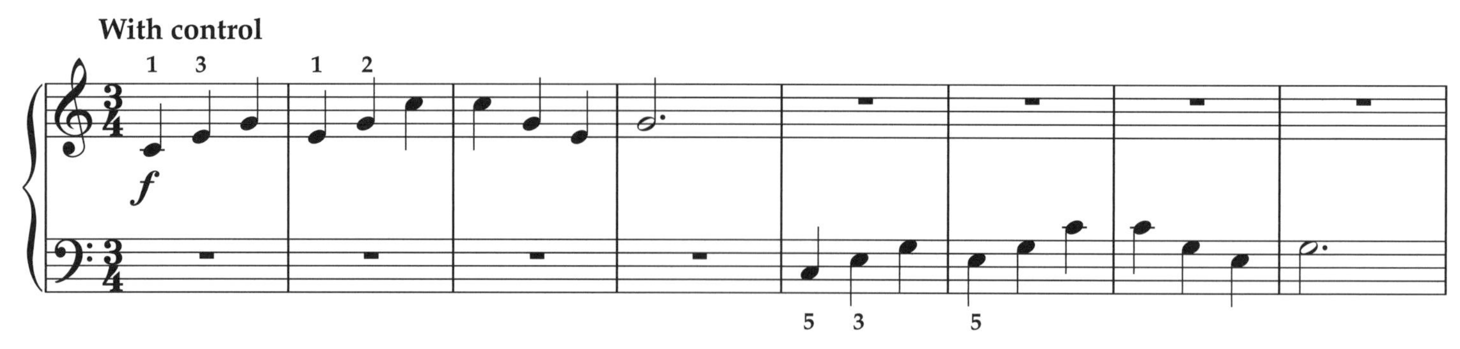

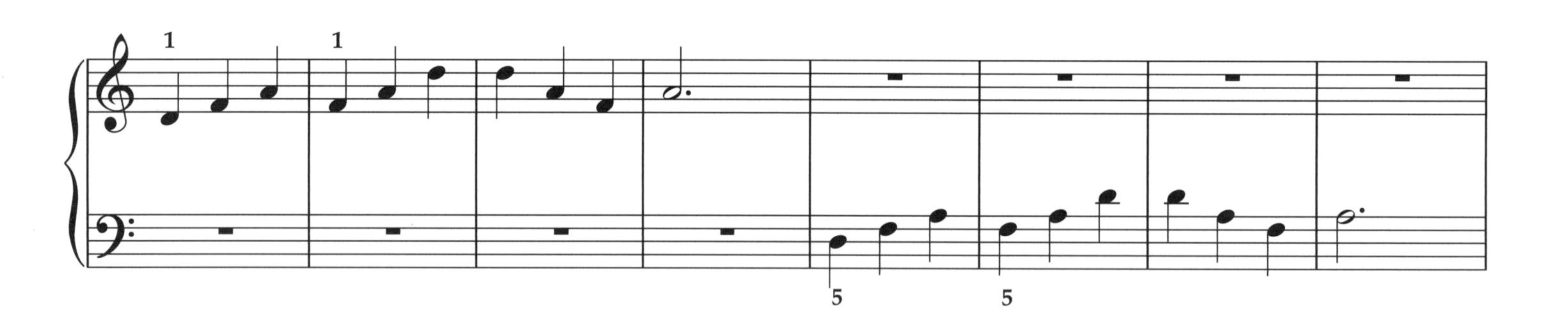

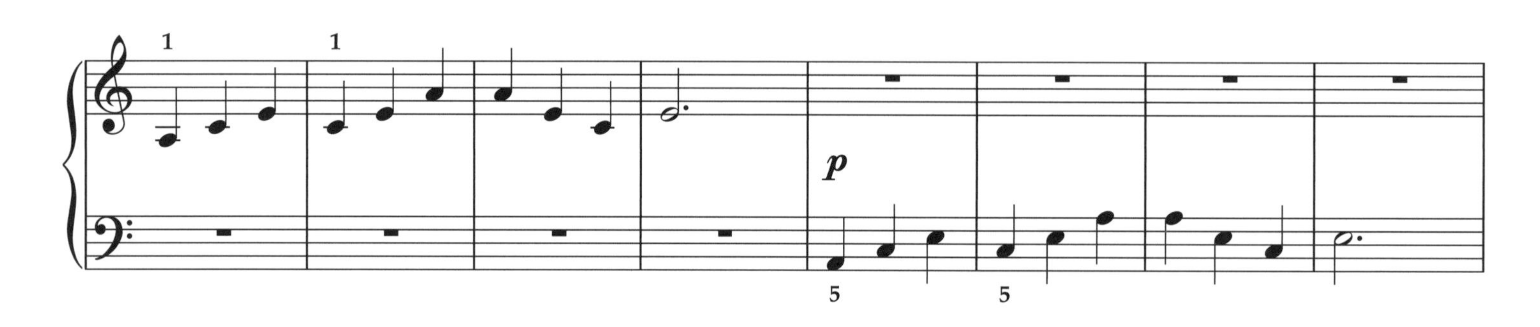

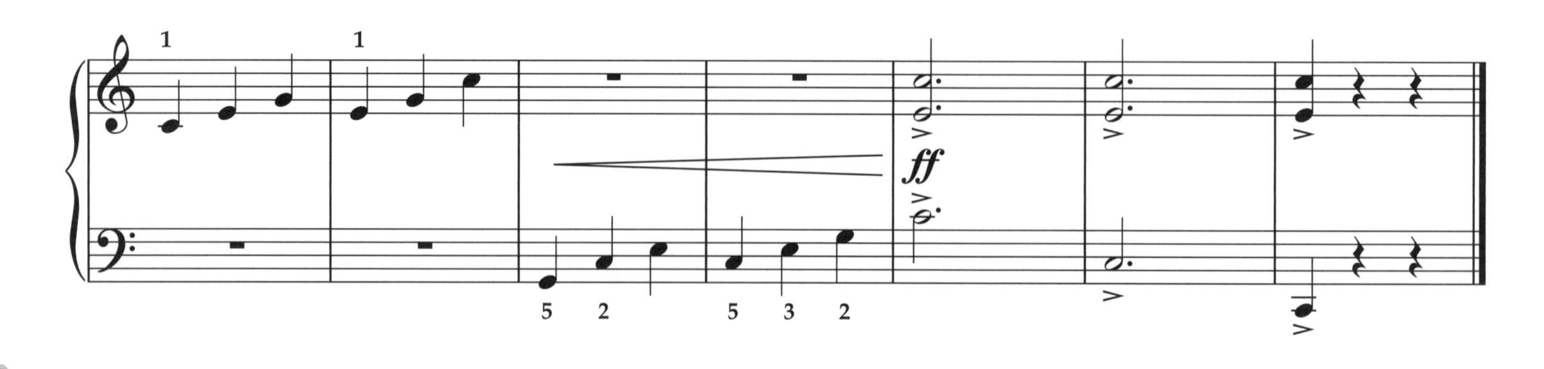

Start by clapping the rhythm of each of these pieces.

Off-beat control 1

Off-beat control 2

Syncopated samba

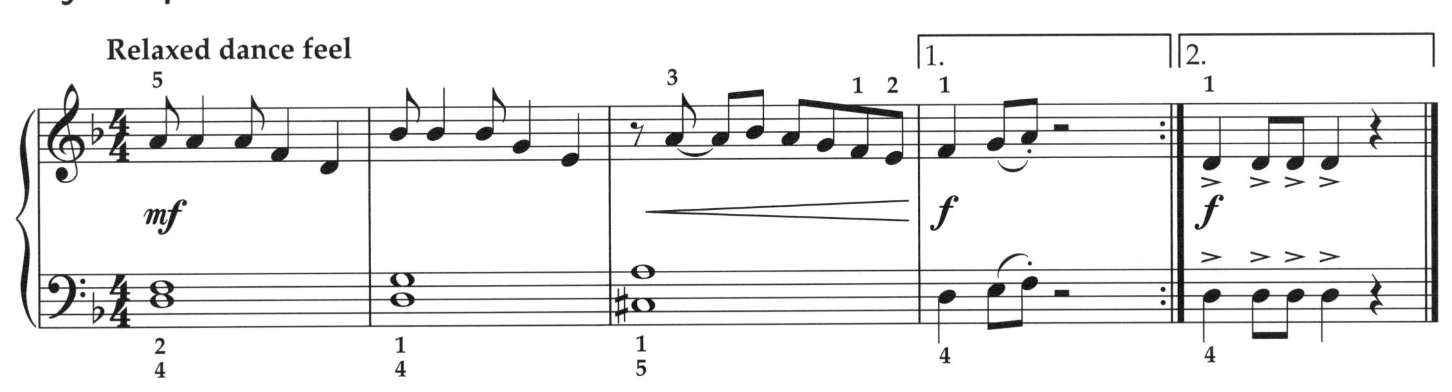

Redbush rag

What key is this in? ____________________

Semiquaver control

Play this at different dynamics: ***p***, ***f*** and ***ff***, as well as legato and staccato.

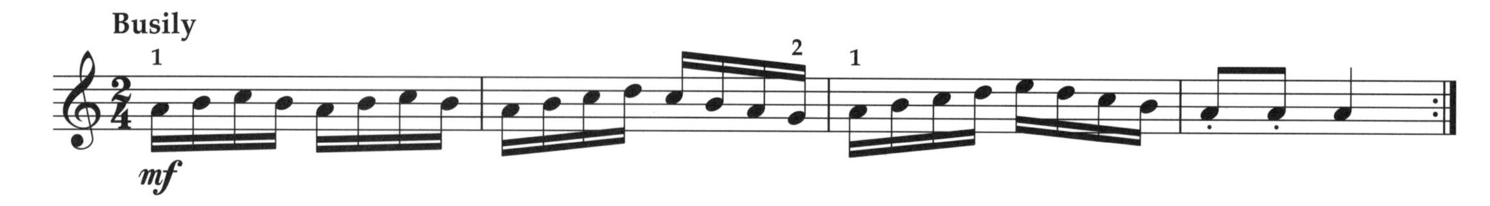

Spinning in space

Make sure you play with light fingers and relaxed shoulders. Remember to breathe!

Lost in space

Dotted control

Try this as a clapping duet – both should play the clapped notes together.

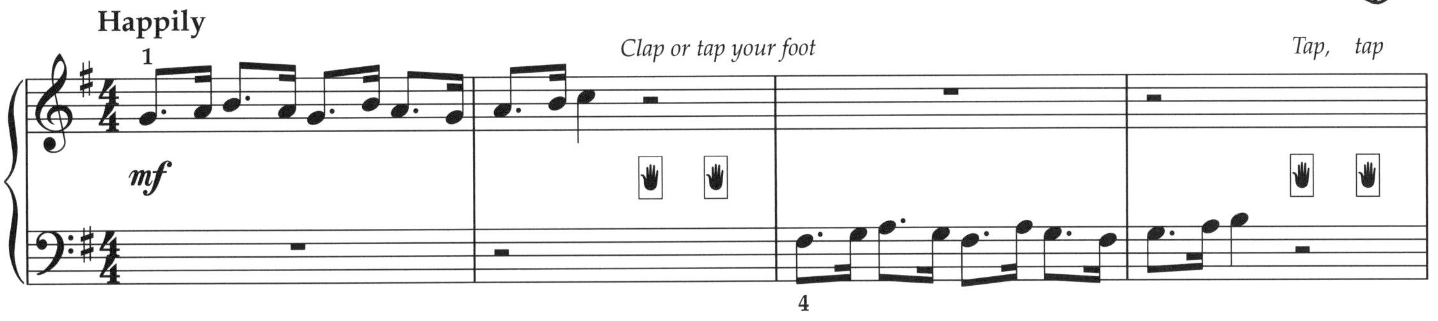

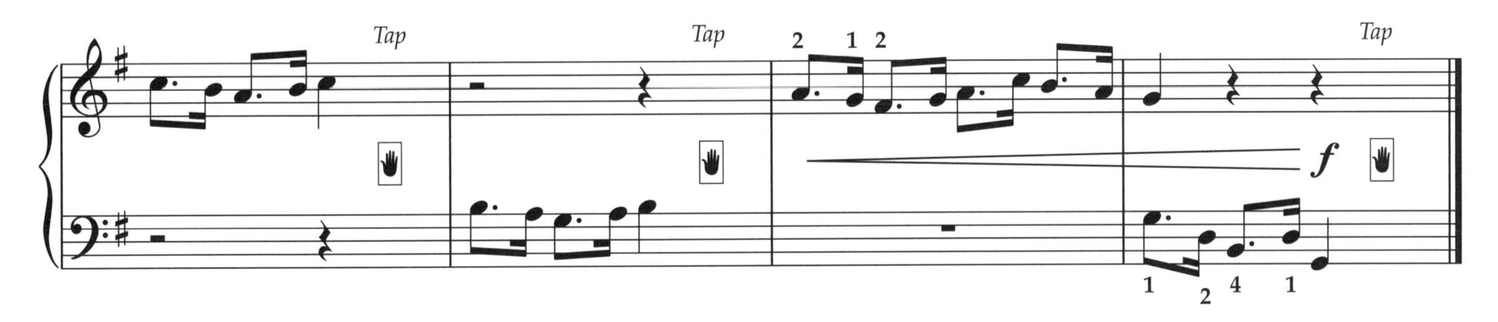

With a stretch

Hopping hippo

Make sure you observe all the expression marks here.

Time control

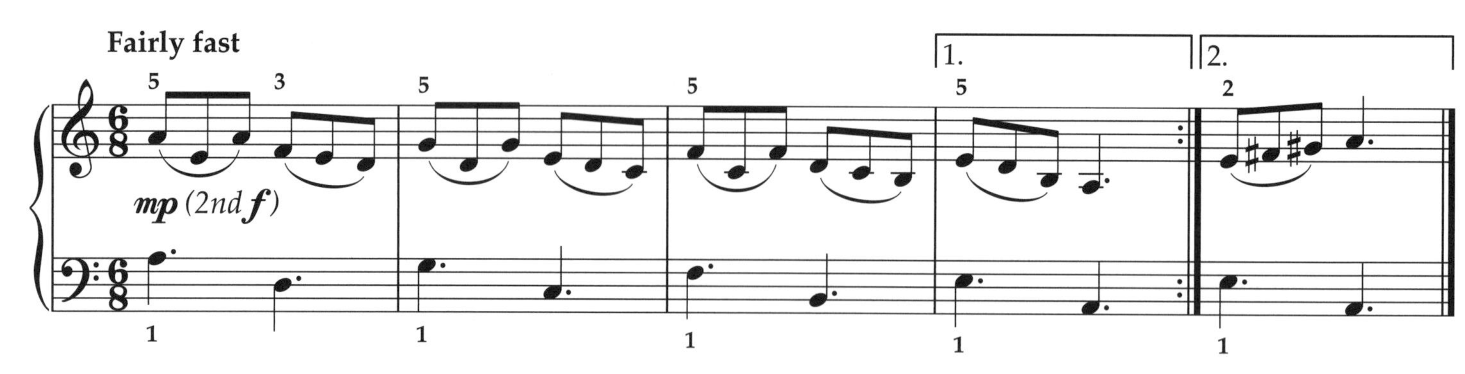

Running around

Try this as a clapping duet.

The lazy cowboy

Your horse is not in a hurry to get home!

These pieces use the right pedal (the sustaining pedal). Choose your own speed. Lift and put the pedal down again where you see ⁀⋀⁀, just after the first beat of the bar.

Foot control

Pedal heaven

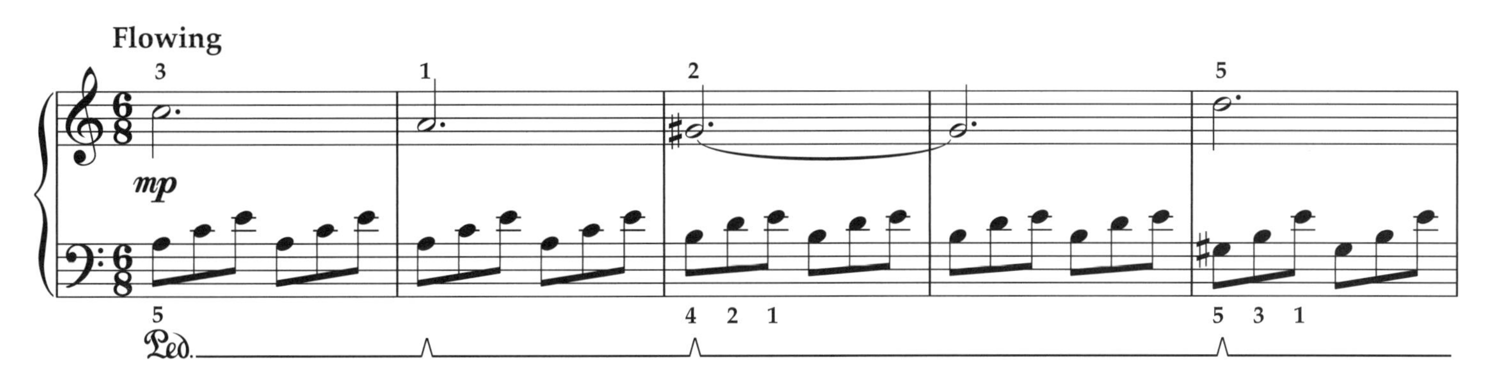

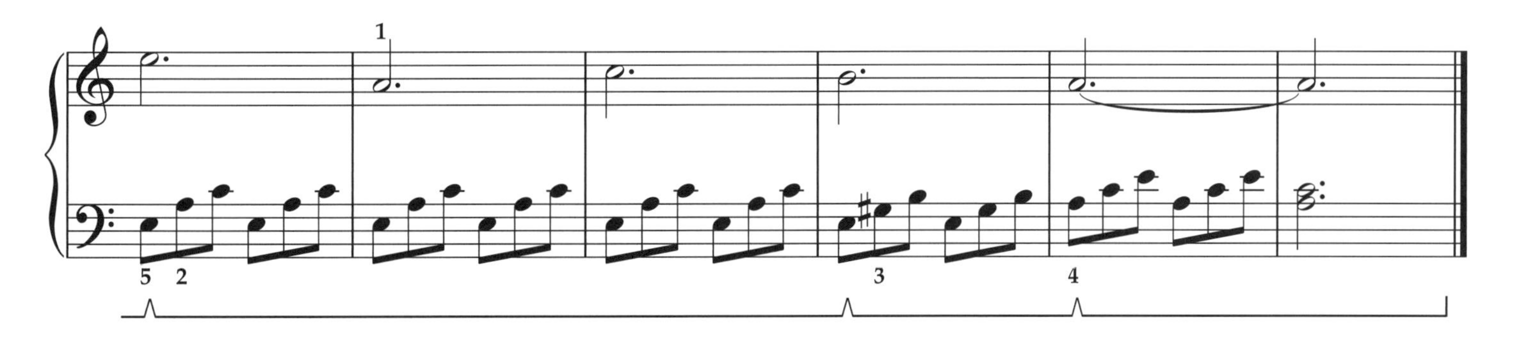

Workout and warm-up!

Use these exercises to get your fingers moving before any practice session.
Remember to relax your shoulders and play confidently.

Finger control

Fingers running up hill

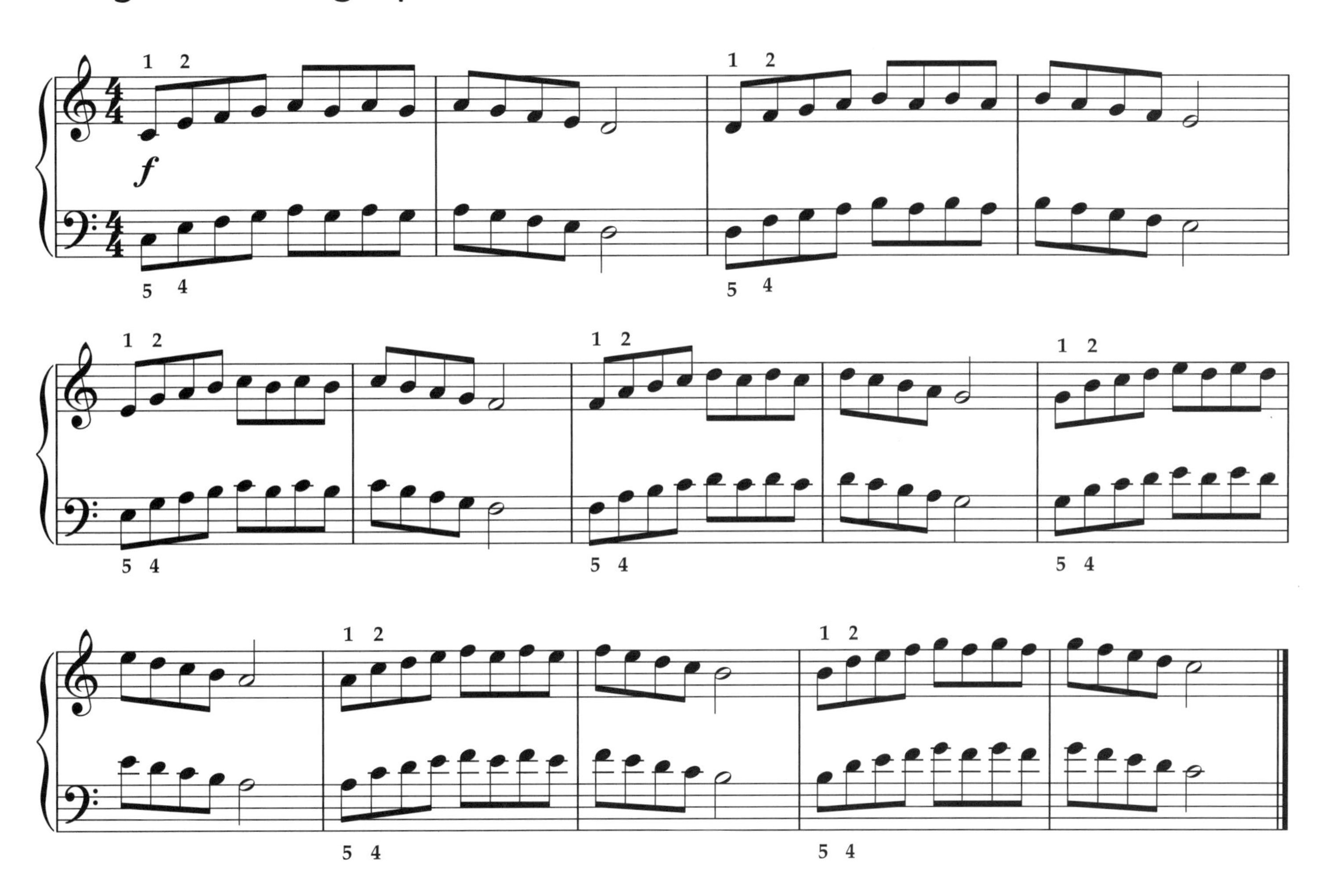

Try both of these at different dynamics and staccato as well as legato.

Fingers running down hill

Also by Pam Wedgwood

Up-Grade! Grades 0-1

Pam Wedgwood's hugely successful *Up-Grade!* series provides fun repertoire for pianists of all ages to bridge the gap between grades. Guaranteed to breathe new life into your piano playing, the varied pieces in these collections are designed to ease you gently on to the next grade.

Up-Grade! Grades 0-1 ISBN: 0-571-51737-4

More Up-Grade! Grades 0-1 ISBN: 0-571-51956-3

Up-Grade! Pop Grades 0-1 ISBN: 0-571-52474-5

Up-Grade! Christmas Grades 0-1 ISBN: 0-571-52953-4

Up-Grade! Jazz Grades 0-1 ISBN: 0-571-52476-1

Up-Grade! Duets Grades 0-1 ISBN: 0-571-53264-0

Really Easy Jazzin' About

The best-selling *Jazzin' About* series by Pam Wedgwood presents vibrant collections of original and well-known pieces for piano in a range of contemporary styles, tailor-made for the beginner pianist. So take a break from the classics and get into the groove as you cruise from blues, to rock, to jazz!

Really Easy Jazzin' About ISBN: 0-571-53403-1

Really Easy Jazzin' About Studies ISBN: 0-571-52422-2

Easy Jazzin' About ISBN: 0-571-53402-3

Easy Jazzin' About Standards ISBN: 0-571-53407-4

Easy Jazzin' About Piano Duets ISBN: 0-571-51661-0

To buy Faber Music publications or to find out about the full range of titles available please contact your local music retailer or Faber Music sales enquires:

Faber Music Ltd, Burnt Mill, Elizabeth Way, Harlow CM20 2HX
Tel: +44 (0) 1279 82 89 82 Fax: +44 (0) 1279 82 89 83
sales@fabermusic.com fabermusicstore.com